In The Library – Sshh!

by Sheree Vickers

Contents

Cast list

In the library

Librarian *(to be played by the teacher)*
Noisy reader 1
Noisy reader 2
Noisy reader 3
Noisy reader 4
Noisy reader 5
Noisy reader 6

The robbery

Robber 1
Robber 2
Shopkeeper
Copper 1
Copper 2

Witches' spell book

Witch 1
Witch 2
Witch 3
Cat

Dear Diary

Reader 1
Reader 2
Reader 3
Reader 4

Trick or treat!

Friend 1
Friend 2
Friend 3
Trick or Treaters

Girl Magazine

Girl 1 (hairdresser)
Girl 2 (movie star)

Comic books

Boy 1
Boy 2

Jumping out of the window

Businessman 1
Businessman 2

Fashion catwalk

Posh lady 1
Posh lady 2
Posh lady 3
Posh lady 4
Models

Scene 1
In the library

Everyone comes on to the stage, takes a seat in the library and starts quietly reading.

Librarian: Now I don't want any silliness while I'm gone. Everyone should be just quietly reading.

Librarian exits.

Noisy reader 1: *[Disturbance 1]*

All: Sshh!

Noisy reader 2: *[Disturbance 2]*

All: Sshh!

Noisy reader 3: *[Disturbance 3]*

All: Sshh!

Noisy reader 4: *[Disturbance 4]*

All: Sshh!

Everyone is quietly reading again.

Scene 2
The Robbery

Robber 1:	This book's great!
Robber 2:	What's it about?
Robber 1:	It's about cops and robbers. I'll show you. *(Jumps up)* Hey everyone! This is a robbery.

Robber 2 jumps up.

Robber 2:	Yes! We've come for the money.

Rest of group stays still, looking surprised.

Robber 1:	Where's the shopkeeper?
Shopkeeper:	I'm the shopkeeper.
Robber 1:	Put everything in this bag.

Gives the shopkeeper a bag.

Robber 2:	And step on it.
Shopkeeper:	Yes sir. Here you are. Please call again.

Shopkeeper sits down again.

Robber 1:   Quick, to the getaway car.

Robbers race around the room in slow motion, while the Coppers jump up and shout …

Both Coppers: Gotcha!

Cops and Robbers freeze.

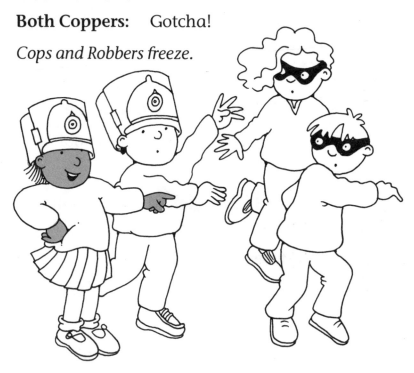

All: Sshh!

Cops and Robbers tiptoe back to their seats, pick up their books and continue reading along with everyone else until …

Noisy reader 5:   *[Disturbance 5]*

All: Sshh!

Noisy reader 6:   *[Disturbance 6]*

All: Sshh!

Scene 3
Witches' spell book

Witch 1:	Shoosh! Shoosh! Shoosh! That's all anyone ever says.
All:	Sshh!
Witch 2:	Don't shoosh us. We're witches.
Witch 3:	Has anyone seen the spell book?
Cat:	Meow.
Witch 1:	Good Kitty. Go and get our spell book.
Cat:	Meow.

Cat fetches spell book.

Witch 2:	Thank you Kitty.
Witch 3:	I've got some new ingredients: bat's wings and lizard's tails!
Witch 1:	What shall we do with those?
Witch 2:	I know. We'll make a spell.
Witch 3:	What spell shall we do?
Witch 1:	Let's turn everyone into frogs.

'Big witch' laughs from all 3 witches.

All 3 Witches: *(With action and movements)*

Witches, Wizards, Lizards' Gizzards
Great big storm and mighty Blizzard
Turn everyone into frogs.

*Suddenly everyone starts hopping around the room
like frogs.*

All 3 Witches: *(In a big voice with clapping of hands)*

Freeze.

Everyone freezes.

Cat: Meow.

Witch 2:   I turn you all into snakes.

Everyone slithers and hisses like snakes.

All 3 Witches: *(In a big voice with clapping of hands)*

Freeze.

Everyone freezes.

Cat: Meow.

Witch 3:   I turn you all into cats.

Everyone starts acting like cats.

7

All 3 Witches:	*(In a big voice with clapping of hands)*
	Freeze.
Cat:	Meow.
Witch 1:	Everyone go back to your seats.

Everyone goes quietly back to their seats.

Witch 2:	And don't remember a thing.
Witch 3:	Unless we say.

'Big witch' laughs from all 3 witches.

All:	Sshh!

Witches and Cat return to their seats, pick up their books and continue reading along with everyone else.

8

Scene 4
Dear Diary

All 4 Readers: Dear Diary

Reader 1:   My dad broke the washing machine yesterday. He opened it …

Reader 2:   … and a great big green slimy monster with huge jaws …

Reader 3:   … started cooking dinner. I said to my mum …

Reader 4:   … I feel sick. Going round and round and up and down.

Reader 1:   It won't wash the clothes.

Reader 2:   We'll have to train it.

Reader 3:   Can I have a go?

Reader 4:   … on the biggest, scariest roller coaster!

Runs once around the room.

Reader 1:   Water was gushing out everywhere.

Reader 2:   Lightning bolts shot out of its eyes …

Reader 3:   ... and burnt the dinner black.

Reader 4:   Blacker than anything I'd ever seen.

Reader 1:   So Mum hit it with a hammer ...

Reader 2:   ... and his eyes turned purple and his tongue was all slimy.

Reader 3:   That's the last time I eat that.

Reader 4:   Talk about SCARY!

All: Sshh!

Scene 5
Trick or Treat! ————————

Suddenly, everyone starts skipping around the room singing

Trick or Treaters: Trick or Treat. Smelly Feet.
Give us something good to eat.
If you don't, I don't care.
'Cos I'll pull out your
horrid hair.

Trick or Treaters freeze in a scary position.

Friend 1: *(To Friend 2)*

Go and see who that is.

Trick or Treaters: Trick or Treat?

Friend 2: Go away, you smelly children.

Trick or Treaters: Trick or Treat?

Friend 3: You're not getting any treats
here.

Trick or Treaters: Trick or Treat?

All 3 friends: Trick!

[Trick 1]

11

Friend 1:	Oh how horrible.
Friend 2:	That's disgusting.
Friend 3:	That doesn't scare me.
Trick or Treaters:	Oh yeah? Well maybe this will …
	[Trick 2]
Friend 1:	Oh how horrible.
Friend 2:	That's disgusting.
Friend 3:	That *still* doesn't scare me.
Trick or Treaters:	Oh yeah? Well maybe *this* will …
	[Trick 3]
Friend 1:	Oh how horrible.
Friend 2:	That's disgusting.
Friend 3:	Aaahhh!!!

All: Sshh!

Scene 6
Girl Magazine ─────────────

Everyone is quietly reading again.

Girl 1: *(To Girl 2)*
What magazine are you reading?

Girl 2: *Girl Power.*

Girl 1: What's in it?

Girl 2: All the latest music and fashion.

Girl 1: Anything on hair? When I grow up
I'm going to be a hairdresser.

Girl 2: When I grow up I'm going to be a
famous movie star.

Girl 1: Maybe I could do your hair.

Goes behind Girl 2's chair and tips her head back as if washing it in a hairdressing basin.

Girl 1: *(As hairdresser)*
Shampoo. Rinse. Would you like
any conditioner?

Girl 2: *(As famous movie star)*
Only a little bit. I've got a big movie
coming up.

Both girls freeze in that position.

Scene 7
Comic books ───────────────

Boy 1:   Batman could beat up Spiderman any day.

Boy 2:   Oh yeah?

Boy 1:   Yeah.

Boy 2:   Spiderman can climb up walls.

Boy 1:   Spiderman can't fly.

Boy 2:   Neither can Batman.

Boy 1:   Oh yeah?

Boy 2:   Yeah!

Boy 1:   Batman has a utility belt that's got everything on it.

Boy 2:   Spiderman can spray sticky webs to catch people.

Boy 1:   Oh yeah?

Boy 2:   Yeah!

Boys freeze.

Scene 8
From rich to poor ━━━━━━━━━━

Businessman 1: How rich are you?

Businessman 2: Very rich.

Businessman 1: Me too. I have millions.

Businessman 2: What are you reading?

Businessman 1: The *Financial Times*. What are you reading?

Businessman 2: *Business Today.*

They continue reading until suddenly ...

Businessman 1: Oh no!

Businessman 2: Oh no!

Businessman 1: I've lost all my money.

Businessman 2: Me too.

Businessman 1: The stock market's crashed.

Businessman 2: I know.

Businessman 1: That means we're . . . poor!

Businessmen look at each other.

Both Businessmen: Aaahhh!!!

Freeze.

Scene 9
Fashion catwalk _____

Posh Lady 1:   Oh, I am so posh. Look at all these fashions.

Posh Lady 2:   That one looks nice.

Posh Lady 3:   We should have a fashion show.

Posh Lady 4:   Bravo, darling. What a wonderful idea.

Both Posh Ladies: *(Calling)*

Models.

Music starts and everyone gathers at the top of the stage in a line. They freeze in model poses and one by one, proceed down the 'catwalk'. When everyone has had a go, they dance around the room as if at a disco. This continues until the Librarian re-enters and the music is abruptly switched off.

Librarian: Who is making all this noise? This is supposed to be a library.

All: *(to Librarian)*

Sshh!

THE END

16